SAM ROSENFELD was for many years a research scientist in private industry. During World War II he worked as a civilian and as an officer for the United States Air Force at Wright Field, Dayton, Ohio, in the field of chemistry.

He holds a B.S. from City College, New York, an M.A. from New York University, and he now teaches science in New York.

Among the author's published works are *Science Experiments with Air, Science Experiments with Water,* four other books on scientific subjects in the "Ask Me a Question" series, and *The Story of Coins* and *The Magic of Electricity.*

About the Book

A drop of water on a rock mysteriously disappears. Where does it go? What happens to it? Does it ever reappear?

High above the tallest mountains and buildings a tiny cloud appears and grows and grows. Is this where our wandering drop of water can be found? If so, how and why has it reappeared?

What causes the cloud to grow and grow and grow, until it is so large that it comes pouring down in a deluge of rain that ruins picnics but makes the flowers happy?

A boy or girl can follow the story of a drop of water in this charming book which combines reading fun with a delightful learning experience.

The ideas about clouds and water and rain as presented in this book are easily understood by the youngster who has already learned to read, as well as by the younger child who likes to listen when read to by an adult, or by an older brother or sister.

No. 8178-462-L

To my friends,
Edith and Nat

A DROP OF WATER

By SAM ROSENFELD

Illustrated by HELEN BASILEVSKY

**SCIENCE
PARADE
BOOK**

HARVEY HOUSE, INC.
Publishers
Irvington-on-Hudson, N.Y. 10533

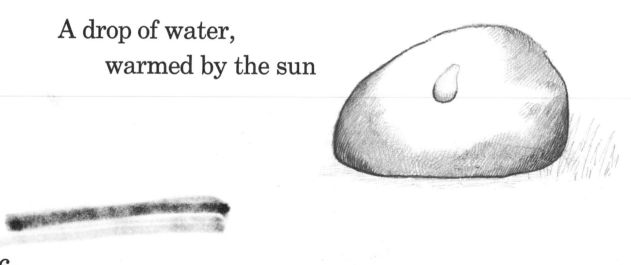

A drop of water,
      warmed by the sun

. . . . becomes smaller

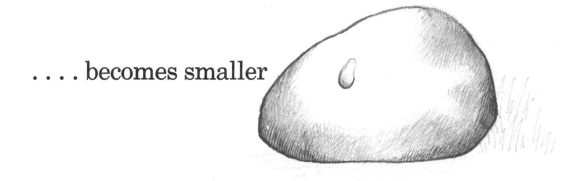

. . . . and smaller

. . . . and is GONE!

Where did it go?
Is it hiding in the wind?
Watch as the wind blows
against the glass
of lemonade.

8

There it is again!
Our drop of water,
   along with many other drops,
   is resting upon the outside
   of the cold glass.

The bright sun warms the glass,
and once more the drop of water
and all the other drops

.... become smaller

. . . . and smaller

. . . . and are gone again!

Night is falling,
and the earth grows cold.
Where is our drop of water?
There it is!

. . . . on a cool blade of grass.

And here and there are
many other drops of water

. . . . on flowers

. . . . on leaves

. . . . and on rocks.

Now we know its secret!
It hides in the warm air
        and comes back again
        when it touches something COLD!

The day is new.
And the sun comes up
and warms the earth.

Again
    all the drops of water
    become smaller

. . . . and smaller

. . . . and are gone.

Now the wind carries the hidden water
higher and higher and higher

.... above the tallest buildings

. . . . above the snow-topped mountains.

Up and up they go,
    half a mile or a mile above the earth—
    or even higher!

The air is getting COLDER.
Suddenly the hidden water
    touches a cold speck of dust
    floating up high.
Shall we be able to see
    the drop of water again?

There it is!
The hidden water has become a droplet
along with many other tiny drops of water.

The cold, windblown droplets
   race above the land and sea.
They find more water
   hidden in the high cold air.
Like old friends,
   they join each other
   and the drops grow and GROW.

And way, way below
some boys and girls at a picnic
look up and see them.
The drops have become
a tiny white cloud!

The small cloud moves
across the sky
.... and GROWS

Now it passes over a great city.

A man looks up
  and sees a bright, white cloud

    . . . . not too small,
    . . . . not too large.

The cloud crosses a field of flowers,
and a rabbit looks up
and sees a great, big, shining cloud

. . . . and scampers happily away.

27

The cloud grows and grows.
It becomes heavier
and moves closer to the warm ground.

The drops of water become larger
    . . . . and heavier
    . . . . and darker
    . . . . and cover the sky
as far as the eye can see.

The children look up
and decide they had better
pack up and leave.

The man looks up
and decides to go home.

32

The rabbit looks up
and decides to run into a hole.

The air can no longer hold up
   the large, heavy drops of water
   that make up the cloud.
Suddenly they fall back to earth as RAIN!

And the thirsty flowers and trees
can drink again.

And so can boys and girls

and men and women.

And so can birds and animals and insects.

Even fish are happy

as rivers are high again.

After the clouds have fallen,
  the sun shines,
  and the sky is blue again.

Now we see

. . . . a drop of water
warmed by the sun.

It becomes smaller

. . . . and smaller

. . . . and smaller

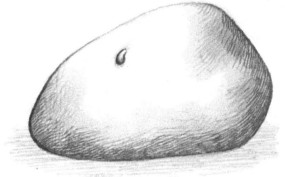

. . . . and is GONE!

BUT IT WILL BE BACK!

About the Author

SAM ROSENFELD was for many years a research scientist in private industry. During World War II he worked as a civilian and as an officer for the United States Air Force at Wright Field, Dayton, Ohio, in the field of chemistry.

He holds a B.S. from City College, New York, an M.A. from New York University, and he now teaches science in New York.

Among the author's published works are *Science Experiments with Air*, *Science Experiments with Water*, four other books on scientific subjects in the "Ask Me a Question" series, and *The Story of Coins* and *The Magic of Electricity*.

About the Artist

HELEN BASILEVSKY was born in Brussels, Belgium, of Russian parents. A graduate of Pratt Institute, New York, with a degree in graphic arts and illustration, she now lives in New York City.

As part of this country's cultural exchange agreement with the U.S.S.R., the U.S. Information Agency in 1963 sponsored an exhibit, "Graphic Arts, U.S.A." Miss Basilevsky toured the Soviet Union as a guide with this exhibit.

DATE DUE
